Your Adventurous Life Awaits

YALA Workbook

Maryann & Brian Remsburg

Lasting Press

ISBN: 978-1-949696-10-3 (paperback)

Printed in the United States of America

Published by:

Lasting Press

615 NW 2nd Ave #915

Canby, OR 97013

Project Management, Editing, and Launch: Rory Carruthers Marketing

Cover and Interior Design: Rory Carruthers Marketing

www.RoryCarruthers.com

For more information about Maryann and Brian Remsburg and Adventurous Life or to book them for your next event, speaking engagement, podcast, or media interview, please visit: www.adventurouslife.net.

Your Adventurous Life Awaits (YALA) Workbook

We are excited that you have chosen to begin applying the *7 Coordinates* from *Your Adventurous Life Awaits* with this accompanying workbook. The content and activities here will help you take the *7 Coordinates* and use them effectively in your life. You will walk through the process of adventurous living step by step and be given ample opportunity to reflect on your journey.

Do not feel that you have to do all the exercises or activities presented here right away. This workbook is a tool that you can re-visit multiple times as seasons or situations in your life arise. Some activities will be meaningful now, while others may apply more to your journey later. Choose the questions and activities on your first visit that resonate with you and help you move toward a more adventurous mindset.

Don't miss out on the application component. It is critical to ensure the content from *Your Adventurous Life Awaits* is not left in a theoretical state but utilized powerfully to help you live your purposeful life of adventure.

Coordinate One: Know Your Zone

"If it doesn't challenge you, it doesn't change you."

—Fred DeVito

Your sense of adventure determines what falls inside your Zone of Comfort, your Zone of Challenge, and your Zone of *That's Crazy.* These zones are not static, but expand as you step up to more challenges and grow into being an adventurer in your own life.

What your adventures look like is not as important as the fact that you are taking on challenges, because this is where growth takes place in your life.

Let's review the three zones before you take time to analyze and apply them to your own life:

The Zone of Comfort

Comfort is defined as "a state of physical ease," "freedom from constraint," and "the state of having a pleasant life." Being comfortable comes easily, and there is little to no stress, fear, or anxiety associated with it. Write down what comfortable activities you enjoy doing.

Example: *Sitting on the couch, reading a book with a cup of coffee* _____

_____

_____

_____

_____

Being in the Zone of Comfort is where you will spend a significant portion of your life. You have a sense of safety and security here, and it would be exhausting to live without this zone. The problem comes when the Zone of Comfort traps you, and you get stuck here. The desire for safety, security, and comfort can easily take over if you let it, which is a problem when you desire to live an adventurous life.

You may find yourself stuck in your Zone of Comfort at times. The activities or desires that trap you in this zone might be good things, responsible things, relaxing things, helpful things, easy things, or even important things. What do you find traps you in your Zone of Comfort?

_____

_____

_____

We are not saying to move out of your Zone of Comfort completely. It's when you get stuck in this zone and rarely venture out that you miss out on the adventures, the thrills, and the emotions that make life feel so much more than just "good enough."

Dead-End Thinking also causes you to stay stuck in your Zone of Comfort.

Dead-End Thinking is any thought that hinders forward progress. It is often a belief about oneself that uses words or phrases like *can't, could never, impossible*, or *too hard*. Dead-End Thinking can cause you to fixate on one option and not consider alternate routes. This thinking is like a person who has turned down a dead-end street and feels stuck because their path ahead is blocked. They may believe there is no possible way to reach their destination.

The list below shares some of the reasons we may get stuck on the dead-end street of the Zone of Comfort. Circle any that apply to you or write your own.

LIMITED BELIEFS	FEAR	BUSYNESS	WORRY
LACK OF CREATIVITY	PRIDE	ENJOYMENT	LAZINESS

Getting Unstuck From Your Zone of Comfort

List time-wasting activities that are comfortable for you, but that you feel are taking up too much of your time, and answer the questions below:

Example: *Watching movies after work*	
1. How much time do you spend here each day? 2. What do you get out of this activity? 3. What suffers because of the time you spend here? 4. What would you recommend to a friend who is wasting their time on this activity?	1. *2 Hours* 2. *Zone out and not think* 3. *Getting life tasks done* 4. *Finish 3 tasks before turning on a movie*
Activity:	
1. How much time do you spend here each day? 2. What do you get out of this activity? 3. What suffers because of the time you spend here? 4. What would you recommend to a friend who is wasting their time on this activity?	1. 2. 3. 4.
Activity:	
1. How much time do you spend here each day? 2. What do you get out of this activity? 3. What suffers because of the time you spend here? 4. What would you recommend to a friend who is wasting their time on this activity?	1. 2. 3. 4.

List productive, positive, or useful activities that you end up spending too much time on because they are comfortable and easy for you, and answer the questions below:

Example: *Meeting network partners for coffee*	
1. What do you like about the activity? 2. What do you avoid because you are doing this activity instead? 3. How could you limit your time spent on this activity? 4. How could limiting this activity help you move out of your Zone of Comfort?	1. *Connecting with people* 2. *Client records and business accounting* 3. *Limit weekly hours spent on connection meetings* 4. *Schedule accounting and organizing time into my schedule directly before a connection meeting*
Activity:	
1. What do you like about the activity? 2. What do you avoid because you are doing this activity instead? 3. How could you limit your time spent on this activity? 4. How could limiting this activity help you move out of your Zone of Comfort?	1. 2. 3. 4.
Activity:	
1. What do you like about the activity? 2. What do you avoid because you are doing this activity instead? 3. How could you limit your time spent on this activity? 4. How could limiting this activity help you move out of your Zone of Comfort?	1. 2. 3. 4.

During your interactions with other people, in new situations, or those activities outside your routine, you may notice your Zone of Comfort grab hold of you, and you feel stuck. Think back to Emmalee and Tyler in *Your Adventurous Life Awaits*, who are stuck in their Zone of Comfort while they ache for more of their adventurous dreams in their life. They want more passion, more joy, and more excitement, but they currently do not have that in their stuck state.

Tyler and Emmalee's response to their Zone of Comfort:

They know what to expect and are comfortable there, so they don't venture out of this zone.

A fear that drives their response?

That they might fail after expending energy on trying something new.

Other negative emotions affecting their decision?

Lack of belief in their dreams and the fact that it could change them and their lives.

How would Tyler and Emmalee like to respond instead?

They would like to take steps to live with more passion and adventure.

Let's explore your responses or reactions to situations or people that you recognize come from your Zone of Comfort. They may not be the most positive or healthy for you or others, but you react this way because they are comfortable.

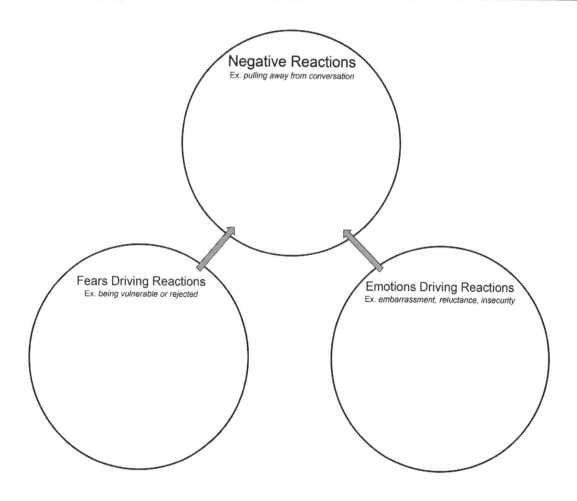

How would you like to respond instead?

Ex. open up to share more feelings

Being aware of what keeps you stuck in your Zone of Comfort is the first step to making a change to move toward your Zone of Challenge.

The Zone of Challenge

Challenge is "a call or summons to engage in a contest of skill or strength," and it may include "special effort." You can challenge your mindset, emotions, beliefs, or activities.

You know you have stepped into your Zone of Challenge because things seem unfamiliar, a little bit risky, and you don't feel as confident here. In the Zone of Challenge, the possibility of failure is staring you in the face, doubts are creeping into your mind, and you have an unsure feeling of what might happen.

_____

_____

_____

For some people, the idea of challenge is exciting. If this is you, your willingness to be uncomfortable or try something that could fail has probably already been growth-producing. Now, you can push yourself even farther into challenge for your greatest results.

For others, the idea of challenge brings fear, uncertainty, and discomfort. If you hear yourself saying things like, "Why would I want to put myself in an uncomfortable situation?", "I'm good," or "Who would want to try something new when this is working?" then you may be settling into your Zone of Comfort. While it may be true that you are "good" or "comfortable," you may be missing out on your full adventurous life by choosing to stay "good enough" or "just comfortable."

Journal about your approach to challenge. Are you someone who is excited by the idea of challenges or someone fearful of them? Can you look back on your life and see a pattern in the way you respond to challenges? Do you have, or have you had, influences in your life who approach challenges similarly or differently than you? What have you learned from these influences?

_____

_____

_____

_____

_____

_____

_____

_____

_____

_____

Rerouted Thinking helps you find a way out of your Zone of Comfort

Rerouted Thinking is changing one's perspective about a situation. Using words like *might, consider, could,* or *hope* demonstrates a belief that there is a possibility. This type of thinking is analogous to the person who turned down a dead-end road, but didn't just stay there or give up trying to get to their destination. Instead, they looked for an alternate route or two that would get them to their desired destination.

Rerouted thinking can greatly impact your view of challenges. If you can see possibilities within a challenging situation, you are likely to find a way to tackle the challenge and see the potential for success in spite of the difficulties you are facing. The more that you practice the skill of rerouted thinking, the more automatic it will become for you in the future.

Practice Rerouted Thinking

Dead-End Thinking	Rerouted Thinking	How Does This Change Your Options?
My in-laws and I cannot get along	Even though my in-laws are different than me, I am going to start listening to them more intently and try not to overreact	It shows that I am responsible for part of the problem and causes me to focus on my responses, not theirs
It's too hard to lose 10 pounds	It's going to be difficult to lose 10 lbs, however, the results will be worth the effort	It provides a motivation to get started and overcome obstacles

ZONE OF

Comfort

Challenge

That's Crazy!

The Zone of *That's Crazy*

Picture yourself accomplishing something that you would love to do, but it is so far out of the realm of possibility that it seems crazy for you to even consider it.

Your Zone of *That's Crazy* should not be forgotten! As you expand your Zone of Comfort and Zone of Challenge, pretty soon a dream that seemed almost impossible might not be as far out of reach as you once thought.

Brainstorm dreams, ideas, and goals that currently sit in your Zone of *That's Crazy!*

Use this space to envision things you would like to aim for in your life, even if right now they are so far out of reach that they seem just downright crazy to think about. Write, draw, sketch, create lists, acronyms, poetry...whatever method gets you envisioning!

Recognize Your Zones Activity

Let's apply our understanding of zones to become more emotionally aware of how the zones have played a role in your life. Choose a time period in your life. It could have been a year ago or it could have been twenty years ago, but the goal is to think about your zones during that time period of life.

Write the year you have chosen or the age you were as a label at the top of the next visual. Think back on your zones during this time period of your life. What was in your Zone of Comfort, your Zone of Challenge, and your Zone of *That's Crazy* during that time?

A Time Period From My Past: _____

Comfort:

_____

_____

_____

Challenge:

_____

_____

_____

That's Crazy.

_____

_____

_____

How have you changed or grown your zones since this time period in your life?

_____

_____

_____

Think of a time in your past, whether the one you just chose or another, when you didn't do something because you were reluctant to enter your Zone of Challenge. Do you have any regrets? If you could go back to that moment now, what would you do differently?

_____

_____

_____

Think back to a time you did venture into your Zone of Challenge. What did you learn from the experience? How did you change or grow? What was the outcome of stepping into your Zone of Challenge?

_____

_____

_____

Is there anything that was once in your Zone of *That's Crazy* that you did accomplish? How did you make that happen?

_____

_____

_____

If you could go back and talk to yourself during a specific period of your life, when would it be and what would you say?

_____

_____

_____

Now, do the same activity, but this time choose a time period in your future. Brainstorm your desired future reality and the way you would like to approach your Zone of Comfort, Zone of Challenge, and Zone of *That's Crazy*. While it may be a challenge to imagine yourself in the future, this activity of envisioning your future self will create an opportunity for you to think about who you would like to become.

Write the year in the future you have chosen to envision, or the age you will be, and label the visual where it says *A Time Period In My Future.* At this time period in your future, what are you hoping will be comfortable for you? What challenges do you hope to be taking on? What will be dreams on the horizon for you in your Zone of *That's Crazy?*

A Time Period in My Future: _____

Comfort:

_____

_____

_____

Challenge:

_____

_____

That's Crazy.

_____

_____

_____

Know Your Zone: Action Step Review

Below are the questions from the end of Chapter 1 in *Your Adventurous Life Awaits*. If you did not take time to answer these questions yet, or want to re-think them to go deeper, we encourage you to do that now.

1. What has influenced you in the past to stay in your Zone of Comfort?

_____

_____

_____

2. What benefits have you experienced by going into your Zone of Challenge?

_____

_____

_____

3. How could growing your zones benefit your future?

_____

_____

_____

Coordinate Two: Explore Possibilities

"The Wright brothers flew right through the smoke screen of impossibility."
—Charles F. Kettering

What do you think of when you hear the word explorer? If you are like us, our mind first goes to people who discover uncharted territory. Explorers, like the Wright brothers, don't sit back and wait for something to come to them; they get up and go look for new paths.

This adventurous mindset of exploring possibilities does not only apply to famous explorers. Each and every one of you can explore possibilities to take your life into a new territory.

What characteristics do you think explorers have that make them adventurous?

_____

_____

_____

Should We Ditch Our Routines to be Explorers?

Before we can be explorers looking for new possibilities, we need to know what our normal routines look like that fall inside the Zone of Comfort that we usually live in. The word routine means it is a repetitive action, done again and again. Things we do over and over usually become more comfortable, without the challenge that they may have once held.

We whole-heartedly support creating and using routines in daily life. We use routines to organize our lives, and try to improve upon them regularly to be as efficient and effective as possible. We also encourage our clients to establish routines based on their goals before they step away from their regular patterns to look for new possibilities.

What are Your Regular Routines?

Daily Routines	Weekly Routines	Yearly Routines
Stop for a coffee on the way to work	*Friday night pizza night and a movie*	*August camping trip with extended family to our favorite campground*

How do these routines impact your life? Do they increase life enjoyment or cause you to feel stuck?

_____

_____

_____

While routines are important for a stable life, if your routines are causing you to feel stuck, you may be in a routine rut. This is when people may start to feel bored and life becomes mundane.

How to Get Out of a *Routine Rut!*

When you are stuck in a routine, or a pattern that you do again and again, it can be hard to see different possibilities. Think of when your car is stuck in a rut. The tires are spinning, dirt is spitting out behind the car as you struggle to get out of the rut that is dictating your movement. Getting your car out of the rut may be difficult, requiring substantial effort and time.

Likewise, imagining something different for yourself, outside of what you already do and know, can be a challenge. Here's one strategy to try. You can use the two words "I Wonder" to help you discover new possibilities. Ready?

Think of an example or two in your life where you feel stuck right now. Maybe the rut of your routine has become so deep that you don't see a way out. Whether it is in work, a relationship, or your leisure activities, you realize that to live an adventurous life, you need to begin looking for new possibilities.

Example:

Every evening my family sits in front of the TV to eat dinner with very little conversation.

_____

_____

_____

_____

_____

_____

The Two Powerful Words of "I Wonder"

When you are ready to spice up your life with new possibilities, the two words, "I Wonder" can help you to look at a situation from a new angle or with a new perspective. Using the *routine rut* you just wrote about, brainstorm "I Wonder" questions that apply to your specific circumstance. Here are a few to get you started:

I Wonder...how could I handle this differently?

I Wonder...how my life could look differently a year from now if I tried something new?

I Wonder...what will happen if I try something new?

I Wonder...when is the right time to make a change?

I Wonder...where I could get the resources I need?

I Wonder...

I Wonder...

I Wonder...

I Wonder...

I Wonder...

Are questions like these typical for you? If not, curiosity is an attribute that will help you see possibilities. When you wonder, you are more likely to see possibilities that are outside the box for you, which is a key to living an adventurous life.

Three Options to Open the Door for Possibility:

1. Step off your Normal Path

When you step off your path, your goal is to take time to enjoy the journey rather than getting to your destination as quickly as possible. Think of stepping off your normal path as a pause in life. It's an opportunity to go on a mini-adventure or enjoy a moment of awe-inspiring wonder.

The possibilities for taking time off your normal path for adventure are virtually endless once you have eyes to see them. Some ideas might include:

- Take coffee to the homeless person on the corner and sit down for a conversation.
- Jump into the lake, instead of just standing on the dock looking at it.
- Stop to watch the colors in the sky change as the sun slips behind the horizon.
- Throw an impromptu dance party in the kitchen.

Brainstorm a few ideas of your own that are right off the path of the normal rhythm and pattern of your days, but would bring adventure to your days.

- _____
- _____
- _____
- _____
- _____
- _____

- _____
- _____
- _____

What holds you back from taking time to step off of your normal path?

_____
_____
_____

Brian has a gift for seeing new possibilities and stepping off the normal path which creates mini-adventures and fun in the moment that has taught our family to try and do the same.

Who do you know that has a gift for taking a step off their normal path?

_____

What have you learned from them? What have you seen in their life that you would like in yours?

_____
_____
_____

2. Explore a Different Path to the Same Destination

The second option for stepping away from your routine is taking a different path to the same desired destination. You are heading to the same place, but now your goal is to explore new paths that you haven't seen or experienced before.

For example, Adam's goal is to have a positive connection with his son. Adam has fostered their relationship by buying him small gifts and toys to let him know how much he cared. This worked well when his son was younger. Now that Adam's son is in high school, he doesn't seem to like or appreciate the gifts very much anymore. Adam is frustrated and not sure how to keep that positive connection with his son. Adam needs to try something new. He needs to explore a different path to the same destination!

Adam's Destination:	Old Path to the Destination:	New Path to the Same Destination:
Positive connection with his son	Buying gifts and toys for his son	Nightly join his son at the basketball hoop and rebound for him

How about for you? What is a goal in your life for which you would like to explore a new path?

Your Destination:	Old Path to the Destination:	New Path to the Same Destination:

3. Try a New Path Toward a Different or Unknown Destination

This third option involves going in an alternate direction in order to achieve a new goal or different result. This choice is all about being intentional about doing something completely different than your usual routine. Being intentional means rerouting your thinking to go outside of what is known and comfortable, which will open up the door of possibility for growth and change.

What are new activities, goals, ideas, ambitions, or objectives that you have never gone for before, but would like to? This new destination could be within any of the domains of your life; intellectual, emotional, physical, marital, parental, spiritual, vocational, social, financial, or avocational. Next to each new destination, think about why that is a destination you would like to head toward.

Destination: _Earn my masters degree in teaching and begin working in a school._

Why? _I want my work to have an impact on others, which is not happening in my current job. When I was in college, I started out toward becoming a teacher and then decided I couldn't make enough money, but have always regretted that decision._

1. Destination:_____

Why? _____
_____
_____

2. Destination:_____

Why? _____
_____
_____

3. Destination:_____

Why? _____

_____

_____

What Gets in the Way of Possibilities?

Obstacles and Challenges:

Focusing on obstacles and challenges can lead us into a dead-end mindset in which failure seems like a foregone conclusion. The fact is that living a life of adventure means there will be obstacles to overcome. There will be challenges that come across our path. There will be failures among the successes. After all, without having some level of challenge, obstacles to overcome, and the risk of failure, it really isn't too much of an adventure, is it?

Reflect back on the three new destinations you listed in the previous exercise. What is holding you back from moving toward those new destinations? Clarify the feelings, obstacles, or challenges that have prevented you from moving toward your new destinations...yet!

Feelings, Obstacles, or Challenges

1. Destination:

2. Destination:

3. Destination:

Fear:

Fear will happily keep you stuck right where you are for days, years, or even your whole life, if you let it! Fear comes at you from many directions. Sometimes fear is right in your face, causing an immediate, physical reaction that is easily detected. Other times it slowly creeps into your life before you even realize and shuts down your ability to see new possibilities.

Fear can be a difficult subject to explore, so take time to journal about the role that fear plays as you strive to live out your adventurous life. What are things that scare you? What are situations in which you feel fearful? How does this fear hold you back from exploring new possibilities and embracing an adventurous life?

_____

_____

_____

_____

_____

_____

_____

_____

_____

_____

_____

_____

How to Overcome Obstacles, Challenges, and Fear

Fight Fear with Hope:

You have probably heard it said that hope is stronger than fear. Hope combats fear by giving you something more powerful to focus upon. You can push past your fears when your hope for a positive outcome is greater than your fears.

For example, Erin has been rejected by men in past relationships, and now, though happily married, is worried that her husband will eventually reject and leave her as well. This fear is expressed through suspicion of her husband. Erin starts by checking up on where her husband goes and who he is with. She repeatedly asks about his commitment level to her and implies that he will probably leave her someday. Erin realizes her fear is starting to cause a rift between her and her husband that is not based on reality. Maintaining hope in having a positive, trusting relationship with her husband, allows her to have a passionate and vibrant marriage, which can help her fight her fear of rejection. When this fear rears its ugly head again, Erin can remind herself that the hope she has is stronger than her fear.

What hopes do you have that can combat the fears you just journaled about?

_____

_____

_____

_____

_____

Hold onto that hope! It will help you see possibilities and then move forward with action in the coordinates to come. Take time to create a concrete representation of your hope combating your fear and post it as an encouragement to not let your fear trap you. If you are a visual person, create a drawing or collage of this concept. If you enjoy the written word, write a story or poem about this happening in your life. If music speaks to you, try composing a song or find one by another artist that speaks to you about hope.

Curiosity:

As stated in *Your Adventurous Life Awaits,* Dr. Partridge's research shows that curiosity can promote cognitive processes, squash stereotypes, and prevent stagnancy and burnout. If you don't think of yourself as a curious person who can see possibilities, but you want to develop in this area, try some of these strategies:

- **"Engage from a place that seeks to understand and not judge.**" Whether it's political, religious, or another opposing opinion that you're passionate about, try to learn something new and understand before making a judgement.

- **"In disagreements, communicate from a place of curiosity.**" Instead of approaching an argument from a place of anger, ask questions, seeking a resolution.

- **"Every day, spend at least 15 minutes getting curious.**" Research a topic you've always wanted to know more about. Go explore a new route you've never taken before. Stop at an unfamiliar store or landmark in your neighborhood.

- **"Schedule a regular lunch, coffee, or drink date with a curious friend.**" We all have friends who ask lots of questions. Learn to be more inquisitive through their curiosity.

- **"Get curious about yourself by asking self-reflection questions."** You'll get to practice this at the end of each chapter and during *Coordinate 7 - Reflect to Grow*. If you want to take it deeper and open more doors for possibilities, be sure to get the accompanying *YALA Workbook* that includes an exercise to help you work through these strategies to grow your curiosity.

What are two strategies that you will try to grow your curiosity?

Strategy #1:

_____

How will you implement this strategy?

_____

_____

_____

_____

When will you put this strategy into action?

_____

Strategy #2: _____

How will you implement this strategy?

_____

_____

_____

_____

When will you put this strategy into action?

_____

Explore Possibilities: Action Step Review

Below are questions from the end of Chapter 2 in *Your Adventurous Life Awaits.* If you did not take time to answer these questions yet, or want to re-think them to go deeper, we encourage you to do that now.

1. What possibilities could be a part of your future and what steps do you need to take to explore them more?

_____

_____

2. What resonated with you most about stepping out of your routine?

_____

_____

3. How can curiosity impact you living an adventurous life?

_____

_____

Coordinate Three: Commit to the Journey

"There's a difference between interest and commitment. When you are interested in doing something, you do it only when it is convenient. When you are committed to something, you accept no excuses; only results."

—Unknown

Commit. Just the thought of this word may bring on fear and trembling. You may take time to move forward with your decisions to commit, whether it entails signing your name on the dotted line, investing time or money, or telling someone your plans.

On the other hand, you may find making commitments comes easily and quickly, whether you are taking an oath, making that down payment, or posting the commitment of your plans in a prominent location.

Regardless of how you come to making a commitment or how difficult the process is for you, it is an important one. In terms of living adventurously, after you know your zones and explore possibilities, it takes the act of making a commitment to step out on a journey of adventure.

Brainstorm Past Commitments You Have Made (successful or unsuccessful)

What Was the Commitment?	Why Did You Decide on this Commitment?
Pledge a monthly contribution to a local non-profit	*I believe in the mission of this organization and using what I have to help others.*

It is possible you don't have a strong *why* for all the commitments listed above. Before making a commitment toward adventure, we advocate knowing your *why*. When you know your *why* before choosing a journey, it makes your adventure purposeful. That is what we at Adventurous Life are encouraging—***purposeful adventures***.

Determining the *why* for your decisions, journeys, and adventures comes from you—your beliefs, values, experiences, faith, skills, and hopes for the future.

Whether you are making a major life decision about a new career, deciding if you should marry the person you are dating, or something much smaller like picking where you would like to go for vacation this year, clarifying your *why* can help you step out with confidence on your adventure. Before making a commitment to a journey that you are contemplating, there are other aspects of commitment to consider.

Investment of Finances Toward a Commitment

Some commitments toward adventure require a financial investment. For us, **adventures are among our favorite possessions**. Often, those adventures have come when we are traveling. Since we have made a commitment to exploring the world as much as possible, it makes sense for us to prioritize investing in travel and related cultural experiences. However, while finding adventure could be bungee jumping halfway around the globe, it could be a heart-pumping experience like white-water rafting right near our home. Our journey could also be seeing or doing something we never have before, like a multi-day bike trip to see our local area from a new perspective. All these adventures require some level of financial investment, but since the adventures are in line with our beliefs and values, this investment makes sense for us.

Since adventures come in so many forms, depending on your individual zone, investment in a journey that aligns with your values and is grounded in a strong *why* is money well spent. Your investment may be toward the adventure of learning, building relationships, growing a business, competing in physical challenges, or even acquiring that dream item.

While we completely advocate being wise with money, we also advocate wisely spending money to live out your commitment to create adventures in alignment with your values and goals.

Describe an adventure in the past that you invested in and considered that investment a wise use of your money. What made this a wise investment?

_____

_____

_____

_____

_____

Have you spent money on an adventure that you felt was a waste of your money? Describe what made it a poor investment for you.

_____

_____

_____

_____

_____

Investment of Time Toward a Commitment

We all have the same amount of time in our days, weeks, and months. While our number of years is not guaranteed, we do choose how we will spend the days, weeks, and months we are given.

Narrowing our focus to invest our time in the commitments backed by a strong *why*, helps us reach our goals. If we don't intentionally use time on our commitments, chances are those days, weeks, and months will slip away.

Let's look at an example before going to the list you brainstormed of your past commitments and picking two to evaluate your time investment toward that commitment.

Commitment:	Get in better shape by losing weight
What specific goal did you want to reach?	Lose 20 pounds within six months
How much time did you give?	Three hours a week of exercise, two hours a week of meal planning and prep
Obstacles:	<ul><li>My birthday was during the second month, so I was tempted with cake and other treats</li><li>Once I lost ten pounds I started feeling good and lost my focus to finish the extra ten, feeling "good enough"</li><li>Negative self-talk, including asking myself why I am working so hard when I will most likely just put the weight back on over the holidays</li></ul>
Was this worth the time invested? Why or why not?	Yes, I learned how much time and energy it took to meet my goal, along with growing self-discipline.

Commitment:	
What specific goal did you want to reach?	
How much time did you give?	
Obstacles:	
Was this worth the time invested? Why or why not?	

Commitment:	
What specific goal did you want to reach?	
How much time did you give?	
Obstacles:	
Was this worth the time invested? Why or why not?	

In making future commitments, what will help you decide if a commitment is worth the minutes, hours, and days that you will give to it before saying YES to that commitment?

_____

_____

_____

_____

_____

_____

Combat Obstacles with Internal Motivation:

Are you highly motivated or do you find yourself struggling to stay motivated with commitments? Your motivation may depend on what you are doing, but when your why is strong it increases internal motivation. Being internally motivated helps us push through when times are challenging.

Look back to your list of previous commitments again. Using a 1-10 scale to rate how strong your internal motivation toward that commitment was and how that affected the success or failure of the commitment:

Your commitment: _____

Your internal motivation:

1	2	3	4	5	6	7	8	9	10

Motivation's effect on the outcome of your commitment? _____
_____
_____

Your commitment: _____

Your internal motivation:

1	2	3	4	5	6	7	8	9	10

Motivation's effect on the outcome of your commitment? _____
_____

So often in life, people choose certain paths due to a sense of obligation. If your *why* is based on obligation, you are working from an external motivator. We would like to encourage you, just as we do with our clients, to move from obligation to motivation.

In *Your Adventurous Life Awaits,* you saw this example of low and high commitment language, that ties in with the ladder of powerful speaking. Your level of commitment language signals where your motivation is coming from.

Low Commitment Language		High Commitment Language
I should exercise more	vs	I commit to cycle 3 days next week
I need to get to work on time	vs	I will leave at 7:15 for work tomorrow
I have to do my taxes soon	vs	I plan to do my taxes on Friday
Let's get together sometime	vs	Let's meet at 10:00 am on Thursday
I'll give it a try	vs	I'm committing to this project for a year
I ought to eat better	vs	I will not eat dessert this month

Which of these phrase starters most commonly come out of your mouth?

The Ladder of Powerful Speaking

What level of commitment are you?

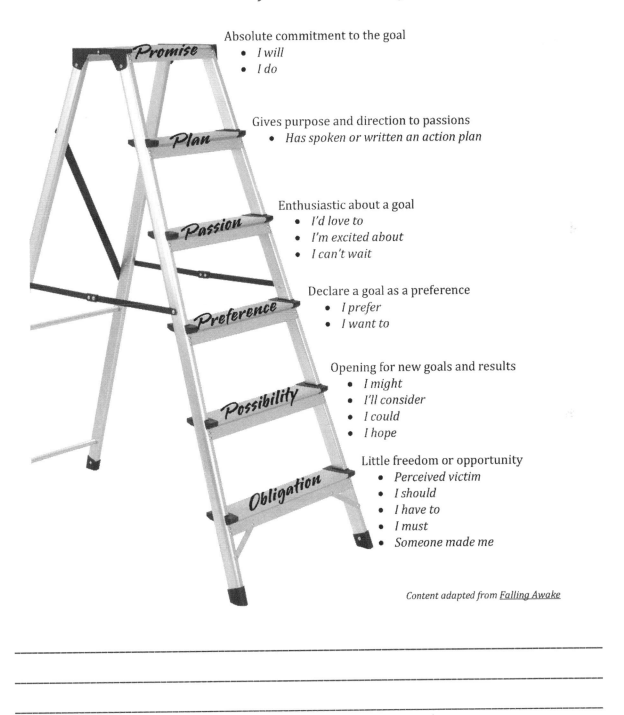

Absolute commitment to the goal
- *I will*
- *I do*

Gives purpose and direction to passions
- *Has spoken or written an action plan*

Enthusiastic about a goal
- *I'd love to*
- *I'm excited about*
- *I can't wait*

Declare a goal as a preference
- *I prefer*
- *I want to*

Opening for new goals and results
- *I might*
- *I'll consider*
- *I could*
- *I hope*

Little freedom or opportunity
- *Perceived victim*
- *I should*
- *I have to*
- *I must*
- *Someone made me*

Content adapted from <u>Falling Awake</u>

_____

_____

_____

Listening to the language you use will signal whether you are operating out of obligation or motivation. The higher you move up the ladder of powerful speaking, the stronger your internal motivation will be.

While acting out of a level of obligation is necessary in life, sometimes we choose to make commitments out of obligation that are not necessary nor even helpful.

Over the next forty-eight hours, listen to the commitment words that you use and write them below. Then evaluate if that commitment is out of obligation or motivation, and take some time to reflect. Is that commitment one you want to keep in your life?

Commitment phrases:	Commitment from obligation or motivation?	Is this a commitment you plan to keep?
I really should organize the garage	*Obligation*	*Realistically, not until things slow down at work*
I will take each of my kids on a date once a month	*Motivation*	*Yes, those relationships are my top priority over work or other commitments*

After examining your commitment language, you may find that certain commitments made from obligation are okay to let go of. Keep in mind your values and goals as you evaluate your motivation and commitments.

Make Your Commitments:

In Chapter 2 of the workbook, you brainstormed possibilities for including more adventure in your life. These possibilities could be found right off your normal path, by taking a new path to a known destination, or rerouting to a completely new destination.

Are you thinking about starting to write that book you have been wanting to write? Maybe you are ready to repair that difficult relationship, or want to take the trip you have always dreamed of. Whatever the possibilities are for you to increase adventure in your life, your first step will be to turn the possibility into a commitment.

These are the three steps we will walk you through to make a commitment that will stick:

1. From your possibilities, choose one commitment you are ready to make.
2. Explore the first R, Relevant, to ensure a high level of internal motivation.
3. Use high-commitment language as you speak to yourself, and a few others, about your commitment.

1. Choose the commitment you want to make, and use the SMARTER goal process to refine it.

Specific - Be as specific as you can with your goal.

Measurable - Your commitment can be documented in a way so that you will know when you have reached your goal. You can also track your progress along the way using midpoints.

A ttainable - Set a goal that is challenging, but achievable.

R elevant - This is your why that makes this goal relevant to your life and values.

T ime-Focused - Having a timeline for completing your goal will help you to stay on track. Also, having a specific time during the day will help you to be more consistent. Associating this goal with a routine that you already have in place (i.e. shower, brush teeth) can remind you to do it daily and increase your ability to be successful.

E xciting - This commitment is exciting to work toward!

R isky - There should be the possibility of failure in your goal, not a given that it will happen.

Write the commitment you are ready to make below.
Now evaluate your commitment using the SMARTER process below.

S	Is it specific?	
M	How will you measure completion? What is a midpoint to measure progress?	
A	Is it challenging, but attainable?	
R	How is it relevant to your life and values?	
T	By what date will you complete it? What time will you do it each day/week? Can you associate it with another activity?	
E	What is your excitement level toward this?	
R	Is it possible that you could fail at this?	

2. Explore the first R, Relevant, to ensure a high level of internal motivation.

Evaluate why you are making this commitment using clarity, strength, and visibility.

Clarity Why are you making this commitment?	
Strength How motivated are you toward this commitment?	
Visibility How will I make my commitment and *why* visible?	

3. Practice using high-commitment language to speak to yourself and others about the commitment you are making.

Write at least three high-commitment sentences about each goal that you are committing to. These sentence starters may help.

I will…	
I commit to…	
By _____, I will…	
I plan to…	
I will not…	

Now that you're done writing and refining your goal, it's time to put it all in one place that you can post using ***clear and powerful language***! We encourage you to make a copy of the following worksheet to use for more commitments, now or in the future.

My Commitment

Commitment:

Completion Date:

Time of Day/Week:

Midpoint	Target Date:

Motivation:

Action Steps to Complete Commitment
1)
2)
3)
4)
5)

How you'll celebrate completion!

How you'll celebrate completion!

There are hundreds and thousands of commitments you could choose from to add more adventure to your life journey. The exercises completed in this chapter will help you make commitments you want to keep, to take the journey of living your adventurous life.

Commit to the Journey: Action Step Review

Below are questions from the end of Chapter 3 in *Your Adventurous Life Awaits.* If you did not take time to answer these questions yet, or want to re-think them to go deeper, we encourage you to do that now.

1. How could you make a change from obligation to motivation in an area of your life?

_____

_____

2. What language do you hear yourself use most often on the ladder of powerful speaking?

_____

_____

3. What possibilities did you brainstorm during Coordinate 2 that you are ready to commit to?

_____

_____

Coordinate Four: Prepare for the Unexpected

"I believe that everyone chooses how to approach life. If you are proactive, you focus on preparing. If you're reactive, you end up focusing on repairing."
—John C. Maxwell

You've probably experienced both the blessing and the curse of having expectations. Everyone with a pulse has expectations at times, either positive or negative. You picture what you think an event or relationship will be like, or you have high hopes for how something might turn out, or you dread what could happen in any given situation.

Living an adventurous life is much like traveling to a new location. You are entering unfamiliar territory where things may be different than what you are used to and do not always go as expected. With any journey there will be frustrations that emerge, misunderstandings about how things work, and disappointment when things do not go as planned. On the positive side, there will also be unexpected thrills, joys, and the beauty of new experiences. Preparing for the unexpected, in travel and in adventurous living, means focusing on what is within your control, preparing for what may come, and appreciating the opportunity for growth along the way.

Preparing for the unexpected means two things:

- Preparing your mindset
- Taking action with details, logistics, and supplies

Preparing Your Mindset:

When you prepare your mindset before experiencing new events, you will be ready to tackle whatever may come your way with a positive outlook and confidence. This means anticipating unpleasant or unfamiliar feelings that may surface. Armed with a mindset ready for the unexpected, you won't be as inclined to hurry back to your zone of comfort. Instead, you will be ready to embrace whatever comes your way, learning and growing in the process.

The concept of preparing one's mindset is common in many different circumstances: before a big race or game, before giving birth, before a big test, before a speech or presentation, before moving into a new stage of life, or before entering a house of worship.

When was a time in your life when you successfully prepared your mindset before an event?

_____

_____

_____

_____

How did the preparation of your mind help you to be successful?

_____

_____

_____

_____

Is there a time when you wish you had better prepared your mindset, and how did that event or time period go with that lack of mental preparation?

_____

_____

_____

_____

Now, let's think about the concept of mindset preparation in terms of preparing for the unexpected. Some people lean more toward expecting the worst, while others optimistically expect the best. If you expect only the negative, you may not be open to see the positive aspects of an experience and accept them when they come. If we expect to have only positive experiences, we may be shocked when a challenge comes and lose our faith or courage.

Which side do you tend to lean on as far as your expectations in your life? Do you usually expect the negative or positive to happen in your life?

_____

_____

While it is important to prepare your mindset for both positive and negative outcomes, we encourage you to focus on the perspective that is usually more challenging for you. We have provided some examples below. Add more that apply to your specific life scenarios.

Prepare Your Mindset for the Unexpected

Statements to prepare your mindset for the unexpected positive outcomes:	Statements to prepare your mindset for the unexpected negative outcomes:
In the middle of a stressful journey, I will also look for beauty and peace.	*Everything will not go as I hope and plan, but I can be flexible when that happens.*
There will be kind people along my path and I cannot wait to meet them.	*Reaching my goals may take longer than I plan, but I will not let discouragement control me.*
I am excited and will look for the learning and growth I will gain from this experience.	*No matter the difficulties, I will draw upon my inner strength, courage, and faith.*

Expectation Is Stronger with Routines and Planned Events

Expectations on yourself, others, and your surroundings are greater when they are a part of your normal routine. This means when something has happened the same way over and over again, you may start to feel that it always needs to happen that way. There could even be a sense of entitlement that something should happen the way it always has.

Another time when expectations can be magnified is when you have planned meticulously in order for something to go a certain way. Think of a wedding or graduation and the amount of planning that goes into those special celebrations. When these well-planned events take an unexpected turn, the frustration and anger that sets in can feel far beyond merely unmet expectations.

Take the next day or two to become aware of when your own expectations cause you to feel frustration, anger, disappointment, or fear when they are not realized. Use the journaling prompts below to process your expectations or journal free flow, if you prefer.

Journaling might include your feelings, the details of the situation, what you notice about your response, or how you could have responded differently for a more positive outcome.

When and where did you notice your unmet expectations?

_____
_____
_____

What were your feelings?

_____
_____
_____

How did you respond?

_____
_____
_____

How would you like to respond next time?

_____

_____

_____

When and where did you notice your unmet expectations?

_____

_____

_____

What were your feelings?

_____

_____

_____

How did you respond?

_____

_____

_____

How would you like to respond next time?

_____

_____

_____

When and where did you notice your unmet expectations?

_____

_____

_____

What were your feelings?

_____

_____

_____

How did you respond?

_____

_____

_____

How would you like to respond next time?

_____

_____

_____

As you become more aware of how you react when your expectations are not met, you may also begin to notice how others negatively respond to their unmet expectations. Learn by watching others who did **not** *Prepare for the Unexpected.* Write what you observed below.

_____

_____

_____

_____

_____

_____

_____

We are not saying that all expectations are negative, not at all! In fact, it would be unhealthy to eliminate expectations completely. We would not reach goals or accomplish much of anything if we sat back without any expectations for our own progress, our day, or our circumstances.

However, the problem comes when we are not flexible and resilient in the midst of our expectations. The ability to be flexible and resilient are two essential qualities that are needed for you to keep moving forward toward your goals.

Prepare for the Unexpected with a Resilient Mindset

An adventurous mindset means that you do not hold onto expectations so tightly that if the unexpected happens and the outcome is altered, the disappointment shuts down future progress. Rather, a person with an adventurous mindset is willing to adapt to unexpected circumstances by looking for the positive perspective and seeking the growth opportunities in the midst of whatever challenge arises. The ability to alter our mindset to see the possibilities hidden under obstacles, helps us to see the positives in any situation.

Now let's examine expectations, either conscious or subconscious, that you may have about the commitment that you made during Chapter 3.

	What is the commitment you made?	Positive things you expect to happen?	Negative expectations about what could happen?	How to prepare yourself to be resilient?
Example:	*Hire two employees by this time next year*	*Work fewer hours*	*I might not be able to give up control*	*If I am frustrated, I will remember my goal*
Your Commitment				

Expectations for Growth

If your expectations are only focused on the end result, you may have a feeling of disappointment when your course is altered based on unexpected circumstances. You may question why you were going down this path in the first place. You may believe that you failed if your expectations took you to a different destination or end result. **If instead, you focus your expectations on growth during the journey, your expectations can be fulfilled no matter what.**

Think about your commitment one more time. What growth opportunities are available, regardless of the final outcome?

	Growth Opportunities Regardless of Outcome
Example:	• *As I train new employees, my patience will grow.* • *I will document processes and procedures I use in order to train employees, which is important to grow the company.*
Your Commitment	

Prepare for the Unexpected: Action Step Review

Below are questions from the end of Chapter 4 in *Your Adventurous Life Awaits.* If you did not take time to answer these questions yet, or want to re-think them to go deeper, we encourage you to do that now.

1. How have expectations impacted your life?

_____

_____

2. What was your response the last time something unexpected happened?

_____

_____

3. How can you develop your adventurous mindset to be more prepared for the unexpected?

_____

_____

Coordinate Five: Embrace the Awkward

"Sometimes you will never know the value of a moment until it becomes a memory."
—Dr. Seuss

If in the process of fulfilling your adventure and purpose, awkwardness comes, we encourage you not to run away from it, but to embrace it.

Deciding to *embrace the awkward* is a necessary step of growth toward increasing adventure in your life. We are not saying you should purposely create awkward situations in order to increase adventure in your life, however, the reality is that in life, awkward moments will occur. It is how we choose to handle these moments that determines their value.

Not all awkward moments are silly and humorous, as some can be intense and emotional. These moments might include times of sickness, relational challenges, or even crisis. This approach does not attempt to minimize the challenge of these intense and emotional times, but it does provide you with a proactive mindset with which to work through difficult moments in the best way possible, and ultimately gain from these challenging experiences.

What awkward moments are memorable in your life? These may have been situations that you got yourself into, or the awkwardness may have been created by someone or something else. Take time to journal about what stands out to you as a few of the most memorable, awkward moments of your life. (There is a little more space on this one in case you need it to process!)

_____
_____
_____
_____
_____
_____
_____

Let's think through those awkward moments in detail a little more:

Awkward Moment:	Your feelings during this event:	What positive result or growth came from this experience?

Through our personal experiences, we discovered a secret recipe for embracing those awkward moments.

 **Recipe**

Dish: *Embrace the Awkward*

From the Kitchen of: *Adventurous Life*

Ingredients:

3 Cups of **Humility**

1 Cup of **Emotional Intelligence**

2 Tbsp of **Humor**

A Dash of **Vulnerability**

Directions:

Mix together all the ingredients. If they are hard to stir or are not the consistency you would like, add a little more of what is needed and keep stirring. When smooth, these ingredients will yield an awkward experience sprinkled with positive memories and the opportunity for growth.

Our society doesn't talk about embracing the awkward nearly enough. The sweet results that come from mixing humility, emotional intelligence, humor, and vulnerability into an awkward situation make developing these skills well worth the effort. Yes, this combination is challenging. Yes, you will still feel awkward at best and completely embarrassed at worst, but living by this recipe, and being willing to embrace awkward situations instead of avoiding them, is an important part of tasting the flavor of the adventurous life.

You may be missing out on adventures because you are not being open-minded enough to embrace a bit of awkwardness in your life. Reflecting upon the four ingredients below, answer the following questions.

Humility	Emotional Intelligence	Humor	Vulnerability

Which one of the four ingredients listed above comes to you most naturally?

_____

How has that skill helped you navigate your life and any awkward moments that have arisen?

_____

_____

_____

_____

Which of the four ingredients could have the greatest impact on your effectiveness and why?

_____

_____

_____

_____

_____

Think of one of the four ingredients that you saw and admired in someone else as they went through an awkward moment in life. Who did you admire? What ingredient did they display and what did you learn from these observations?

_____

_____

_____

_____

_____

When was a time you noticed one of these ingredients missing in someone else's life during an awkward moment?

_____

_____

_____

_____

How did that missing ingredient affect that person or others?

_____

_____

_____

_____

What Causes You to Reject Awkwardness?

Do you find yourself actively resisting, rejecting or avoiding awkward situations? Why do you think you do this? Look at the list below and circle the reasons that resonate strongest with you.

Rejection	Embarrassment	Lack of Control
Feeling Stupid	Lack of Confidence	Standing Out
Looking Foolish	Pride	Insecurity
Impatience	Lack of Information	Looking Incompetent
_____	_____	_____
_____	_____	_____

Write about one or two of these reasons and describe how they have had a negative impact on your life, possibly by keeping you from trying something new or affecting a relationship.

_____

_____

_____

_____

_____

_____

_____

How could you benefit from addressing these reasons head on and not letting them continue to control you in the future?

_____

_____

_____

_____

_____

_____

_____

List three action steps to push yourself forward in learning to _embrace the awkward_:

(Action steps could include situations you previously resisted, conversations you have shied away from, or ways you have not put yourself out there to do or try something new.)

1. _____
   _____
   _____

2. _____
   _____
   _____

3. _____
   _____
   _____

Implementing these action steps will help you live your purpose and passion. If you always run from awkwardness, you may not experience the full growth that comes from living your adventurous life.

Embrace the Awkward: Action Step Review

Below are questions from the end of Chapter 5 in *Your Adventurous Life Awaits.* If you did not take time to answer these questions yet, or want to re-think them to go deeper, we encourage you to do that now.

1. What is your typical response to awkward situations and how is that working for you?

_____

_____

2. Which ingredient in the recipe could you increase to better handle awkward moments?

_____

_____

3. Who do you know who embraces the awkward well, and what could you learn from them?

_____

_____

Coordinate Six: Persevere to Your Purpose

"Perseverance must finish its work so that you may be mature and complete, not lacking anything."
—James 1:4

While the adventurous life is punctuated by moments of glory, there are also the tedious and difficult tasks that make it all possible.

Let's face it, adventures can be difficult to accomplish! We start with grand ideas and plans, but we find the mountaintop experiences come only after hours or days of difficulties. Challenges along the way can bring discouragement, exhaustion, and frustration that might cause you to give up on your commitment.

In our own lives, we chose to persevere on long hikes, through parenting, from mile nineteen to twenty-six of our marathon, when moving to another country, while writing books, on 100-mile bike rides, as entrepreneurs, and throughout challenging relationships. How about for you? What are some of the events, challenges, and adventures in your life, either currently or in the past, that require perseverance?

- _____
- _____
- _____
- _____
- _____

Both of us have worked to persevere and push ourselves past our 40%. Remember that number? According to the philosophy popularized by Dave Goggins, a Navy SEAL, when an individual thinks they have given their all, in actuality they have only depleted 40% of their potential.

"Many of life's failures are people who did not realize how

close to success they were when they gave up."

—Thomas Edison

Like the British cycling team under Sir Dave Brailsford, who used small gains to add up to monumental success, what are small action steps you could take to get closer to reaching your commitment?

1. _____

2. _____

3. _____

Does this mean you are guaranteed success if you can push past your 40% and persevere?

Not at all! However, the chances of success are so much greater with perseverance. Even if you don't reach your destination, so many other benefits can be gained when you persevere.

In our lives, whenever we persevered, we learned lessons we did not anticipate, strengthened our character, built up stamina, and had a greater appreciation for the situations where we did get the results we were seeking.

When was a time that you persevered, but you didn't get the result you were hoping for?

_____

_____

_____

_____

_____

What other lessons did you learn from your perseverance?

_____

_____

_____

_____

_____

Mindset Strategies for Perseverance

Developing an adventurous mindset will guide you toward perseverance. These three mindset strategies are key: visualize your *what*, revisit your *why*, and focus on gratitude.

Using either the commitment you chose in Chapter 3, or another commitment you are working toward, think about the following questions related to visualizing your *what* and revisiting your *why*.

Visualize Your *What* and Revisit Your *Why*

Commitment:	
Write clearly what it is you want.	
Is your plan visible? If not, what can you do to make it more visible?	
Why did you choose this commitment and how strong is your reason?	
What obstacles are in the way of your commitment?	
Who/what can encourage you when you lose sight of your *what* or *why*?	

As you notice in the last question, we challenge you to find one encouraging person to explain your commitment to and why you chose it. Ask this person to help you visualize your *what* and re-visit your *why*.

Who will you talk to about your commitment? _____

When will you talk to them? _____

Gratitude Grows Perseverance

Practicing gratitude can be a simple act, yet can have such a positive impact on our lives in many different ways, including the ability to be perseverant. Let's take a few minutes to focus on gratitude.

What are You Grateful For?

People in your life:	
Goals you reached:	
What you have been given:	
Lessons learned from challenges:	
Surprises you didn't expect:	
Your strengths:	
Things you did not get (Looking back, you are so glad you didn't!):	

Michael Hyatt's three points for gratitude from his article, *Why Giving Thanks Gives You an Edge,* helps us go deeper in terms of using gratitude as a vehicle to help us carry on and persevere.

1. Gratitude keeps us hopeful, which is an important component to perseverance. Without hope, the ability to stay strong and keep moving forward is virtually gone. Think about a time when you were grateful for something which produced hope for the future. How did that hope help you to persevere?

_____

_____

_____

_____

_____

2. Gratitude reminds us that we have agency. Remembering the people who have helped to teach us, lift us up, motivate us, or give us advantages helps us to be grateful. Agency, or the freedom to act independently and make choices, comes from the help and support of others.

Who are you thankful for? List three people who have been part of your personal journey and have helped you be the person you are today.

1. _____ 2. _____ 3. _____

How did each of these people support you and have an impact on your life?

_____

_____

_____

_____

_____

It is rare for people to get to hear about the impact they have made on others. Take this opportunity to say thank you and share your gratitude for these three people who impacted your life.

Why not take them out to dinner, write a card, give them a call, or send a gift to tell them what they did or said that had an impact on your life? Write down your plan, including how and when you will share your gratitude with each person listed above. Of course, this gratitude exercise may extend far beyond these three, as gratitude is a beautiful gift to give!

1. _____

_____

2. _____

_____

3. _____

_____

3. Gratitude expands our possible responses by slowing down negative emotions and replacing them with positive ones. Gratitude helps us to appreciate what we have, which brings along with it feelings of positivity, openness, and kindness. With these positive emotions, we have more responses at our fingertips in situations where we are grateful. Having a multitude of responses readily available when the going gets tough helps us to persevere.

Think of difficult or challenging moments you have gone through. What were the negative emotional responses you felt? If your response was fueled by these negative emotions, your choices may have felt incredibly limited. If you are able to broaden your responses using gratitude, the positive outcome could look very different.

Using Gratitude to Expand Responses

Negative emotions that come without a focus on gratitude:	Positive emotions that come with gratitude:
Frustration and anger when I am stuck in traffic due to road work.	*Appreciation for the roads I drive on that are pothole free with lines to keep me safe and the crew working outdoors to make this happen.*

Rerouted Thinking

It can be your own dead-end thinking that holds you back and prevents you from persevering toward your goal. If this is the case, your thinking needs to be rerouted. Rerouted thinking helps you overcome the obstacles in your mindset, which you may find are the same themes cropping up again and again in different areas of your life. Learning to reroute your mindset with positive thinking and the little word *yet*, can make all the difference.

Use the following chart to identify any dead-end thinking you have that may stop you from moving forward with commitments in your life. Then reroute your thinking to see around obstacles.

Dead-End Thinking	Rerouted Thinking
My relationship with my boss will never get better.	*With better communication and by focusing on the positives, I can improve my relationship with my boss.*

Dead-end thinking can come out as negative self-talk. You want to reroute that talk by speaking truth to yourself positively and with kindness, just like you would to a friend or family member who was stepping out toward a new commitment. What words could you say to yourself that are encouraging and supportive?

_____

_____

_____

Do You Need Support to Persevere?

Complacency, fear, and dead-end thinking can quickly attack anyone, no matter how successful. Coaches support their clients by helping them gain clarity about their goals and then guiding them toward continued growth through a series of small, achievable action steps.

If perseverance is an area where you could use support, we would love to work with you. We are tenacious in reaching our own dreams and would be honored to help you do the same. Our contact information is at the end of this workbook and we at Adventurous Life are ready to help you persevere toward your own adventure.

Persevere to Your Purpose: Action Step Review

Below are the questions from the end of Chapter 6 in *Your Adventurous Life Awaits.* If you did not take time to answer these questions yet, or want to re-think them to go deeper, we encourage you to do that now.

1. To grow perseverance, which mindset strategy of visualizing your what, revisiting your why, or focusing on gratitude, would help you the most?

_____
_____

2. What dead end thinking would be helpful for you to reroute?

_____
_____

3. What is an action step you could take right now to persevere?

_____
_____

Coordinate Seven: Reflect To Grow

"The more reflective you are, the more effective you are."

—Hall and Simeral

Each time you reflect on an adventure, you will learn and grow from it. This will help you to journey farther into your zone of challenge on your next adventure. By following this process of reflection at the end of the six coordinates, you will push yourself toward growth and go into territory where your adventurous life awaits.

Reflection that leads to growth and change in your life, takes time and honesty. Time involves intentionally allotting time to reflect during your days, as well as having the patience to invest in the process. Honesty is about being authentic with yourself about your feelings.

If you have not often taken time for reflection in the past, take a moment to think about what holds you back from this important step toward helping you reach your potential. Could the areas of either time or honesty be part of what makes reflection personally challenging?

_____

_____

_____

_____

_____

This process of reflection and growth can be uncomfortable or even painful, just like in the example of pruning the tree in our backyard. You may need to cut away negative mindset, emotions, or actions in order to bear more positive fruit in your life, which will serve you better.

Are there times when your mindset, emotions, or actions are the master of you and actually working against you?

Examples: negative self-talk, unrestrained anger when I hurt others with my words, poor time management, distractions, or procrastination.

_____

_____

_____

_____

_____

_____

_____

Take time to reflect on how your mindset, emotions, and actions are serving you positively to achieve the life you want.

_____

_____

_____

_____

_____

_____

_____

Self-Reflection

The questions above are examples of self-reflection, but there are many methods available for processing your thoughts and feelings. You can allow your reflection to flow freely, processing as you create, through journaling, artistic expression, music, narrative stories, or poetry, for just a few examples.

Which style of free flow self-reflection interests you the most?

_____

What is your experience using this style and how did it work for you?

_____

_____

What other forms of self-reflection would you like to try either from the list above or something else you have thought of?

_____

_____

Self-reflection can also be more formal. Some ideas could include:

- Learn more about a topic (such as anger, fear, or rejection) and then reflect on yourself in light of the new information you learned.
- Think of a recent event or experience that was in your Zone of Challenge and reflect more formally with one or two relevant questions from the list below.

Self-Reflection Questions:
What thoughts did I have?
What were the emotions I felt from those thoughts?
What underlying beliefs fed my thoughts and emotions? Are these true?
Are my thoughts, emotions, or beliefs helping accomplish my goals?
How did I respond in this situation?
What caused me to respond like I did?
What thoughts will help me to respond how I desire in a future situation?
Your question:
Your question:
Your question:

- Go deeper by self-reflecting more formally about a "journey" you have been on. Whether fun or difficult, chosen by you or chosen for you, you can grow from this journey using reflection.

What Journey Will I Reflect On?		
My Performance:	What success did I experience on this journey?	
	Were there failures that I encountered?	
My Presence: (demeanor, personality, knowledge, and spirit)	Did I show up how I wanted to during this journey?	
	What was positive about my presence?	
My Feelings:	What are my feelings about the experience as I look back on it now?	
	Any emotions I expected to feel that I did not?	
My Learning & Growth:	What did I learn about myself on this journey?	
	What will I do with the information I learned?	

- Create a list or chart to evaluate or to process. The following T-chart is a simple way to categorize information to be used with a multitude of self-reflection topics including:

  - Pros & cons in decision making (see example below)
  - Strengths & weaknesses
  - What went well & what could be improved in a given situation
  - What people say about you vs. how you feel about yourself
  - Confidence builders vs. confidence breakers
  - Energizers vs. de-energizers
  - Dead-end to rerouted thinking

Topic: Should I volunteer time at a local homeless shelter?

Positive Outcome - Pros	Negative Outcome - Cons
• Satisfaction in helping others who need it • I can choose the amount of time I volunteer • I can use my skill of meeting new people • I will start taking action on my desire to help others. • My children will hopefully be influenced to serve others as well • This gives me the opportunity to give back as others have helped me	• I don't want to put myself at risk as I am not sure of the safety and health of the situation • I could embarrass myself or say something wrong as I have not talked with the homeless much before • The time might conflict with my son's soccer practice, so I would have to get someone to help me coach • This would take more energy, which I already feel low in • What if I don't like it?

Topic:_____

Use a blank T-chart in your journal for any of the self-reflection ideas listed above:

- Reflect on your progress toward the commitment you chose in Coordinate 3. Are you making progress toward your commitment? Is anything holding you back? Does anything need to be changed for you to be more effective?

Simple Ask

Write down five people you trust to give you honest feedback and observations on one of the topics you chose for self-reflection. Getting an outsider's opinion will give you a more indepth picture of yourself in regards to that topic.

1.

2.

3.

4.

5.

How and when will you ask them for their feedback and observations?

_____

_____

Assessments

We use the Core Values Index (CVI) assessment and report with our clients. The power of the CVI to give an understanding of core motivators, what energizes and de-energizes an individual, as well as conflict points is a valuable tool. You are invited to take the free version of the CVI with a limited snapshot of your core values. If you would like to go deeper in your understanding of the core values and how this information can transform your understanding of yourself to thrive in your life, you are invited to purchase the Adventurous Life CVI package. This powerful package includes the assessment, your individualized CVI report in full form, and a video series we created to explain each core value in detail that will help you in understanding, productivity, in relationships, and as part of teams. You can find both the free version and our video package at our website: adventurouslife.net.

Look at the resource section at the back of the book for a full list of assessments. Choose one you feel will be most valuable to support you as you move forward.

Which assessment will you choose? _____

When will you schedule the time on your calendar to do it? _____

After Reflection is the Time to Celebrate!

Celebrations for meeting goals can be overlooked or forgotten. Just as we celebrate monumental moments at graduation or wedding time, we want to celebrate how far we have come toward an adventurous life as well. It can be tempting to move on to the next challenge without pausing to acknowledge your accomplishments and recognize the forward progress you have made. When you take time to celebrate, you solidify your commitment to continuous accomplishment and growth, feeding your desire for more positive steps in the same direction in the future.

Acknowledge Accomplishments

How have you personally grown over the last _____**year**_____? (Choose the time frame that best fits your specific reflection):

_____
_____
_____
_____

What are positive steps you took in your life during this last _____**year**_____?

_____
_____
_____
_____

What is something that you did during the last _____**year**_____ that you feel proud of?

_____
_____
_____
_____

How have you had a positive impact on others during the last _____**year**_____?

_____
_____
_____
_____

Have you taken time to celebrate one of these accomplishments? If not, what will you do next week to take time out of your normal routine to celebrate?

_____

_____

_____

_____

Did you have a hard time coming up with a celebration? Many people get stuck when it comes to celebrating themselves. If you are having a hard time generating ideas to celebrate yourself, try imagining what you would do to celebrate the accomplishments of a friend or family member. We do encourage celebrations that are in line with your goals and values. For example, if you are celebrating losing weight, don't use a sweet treat for your celebration, as it goes against the accomplishment you have attained. Here are a few ideas to get you started. At the bottom of the idea page, add your brainstorming for personal celebrations:

Pamper yourself (massage, pedicure, a nap, or bubble bath)

Go somewhere you have wanted to go (beach, movies, or favorite restaurant)

The gift of time (An hour to yourself to do What you want to do!)

Shopping!
(Give yourself an amount that fits with your budget to treat yourself)

Throw yourself a party! (Dinner out, dance party in the house, game night with friends!)

Your Ideas to Celebrate...

Reflect on Reflection

By making it this far, you have shown you are a person who places a high value on personal growth. Is there anything that it would take for you to increase your value on personal growth ever higher?

_____

_____

_____

_____

Reflect To Grow: Action Step Review

Below are questions from the end of Chapter 7 in *Your Adventurous Life Awaits.* If you did not take time to answer these questions yet, or want to re-think them to go deeper, we encourage you to do that now.

1. What new insights do you have about the value of growth?

_____

_____

2. How could reflection help you to step out in future adventures?

_____

_____

3. What reflection strategies are you open to trying over the next week?

_____

_____

About the Authors

Brian and Maryann Remsburg, founders of Adventurous Life, seek to adventurously live out their life purpose and empower others to do the same through life coaching. They each have training as certified coaches with the International Coach Federation (ICF), combined with Master's degrees, Brian in Educational Leadership and Maryann in School Counseling. Their coaching builds upon almost two decades of work in the world of international education. Their training and experience, both personally and professionally, gives them a unique skill set and mindset to support their clients toward adventurous living.

They have been married for almost twenty-five years, eighteen of which were spent working internationally in Kenya, Saudi Arabia, and South Korea. Living and working with individuals from all over the world, growing through the adventures and challenges of the expatriate lifestyle, and traveling to more than forty countries were transformational in the personal growth that led them to their current work.

Their four kids were along for most of these journeys and grew right along with them as adventurers that Brian and Maryann are so proud of. Their family grew multiculturally with their oldest born in Kenya, their second born in Saudi Arabia, and their youngest two born and adopted from Ethiopia. Their children were raised with passports full of visa stamps, friends of all colors and nationalities, and the concepts of the *7 Coordinates* woven throughout their childhoods.

Both are passionate followers of Jesus who seek to live out their faith and purpose. When Brian isn't pouring into his family or clients, he loves to ride his motorcycle, go exploring, play almost any sport, and let his creativity come out in wood-working and other projects that grace their home. He was an amazing support to Maryann as she wrote her first book, *Chosen for Such a Time: Terrorism in the White House*, which is available on Amazon. Besides writing, Maryann loves great conversations over coffee, cheering on her kids at their games, and outdoor adventures, including triathlons, hiking, and paddleboarding.

Being in new environments, and often, uncomfortable situations as adventurers, business owners, and travelers, have grown Brian and Maryann to see the value of daily choosing adventure in their lives. They would be honored to travel alongside you on your journey toward adventurous living.

Made in the USA
Middletown, DE
18 June 2022

67082980R00053